Mood Music

FIFTEEN IMPROVISATIONS FOR ORGAN

Colin Mawby

Kevin Mayhew

We hope you enjoy *Mood Music.*
Further copies are available
from your local music shop or Christian bookshop.

In case of difficulty, please contact the publisher direct by writing to:

The Sales Department
KEVIN MAYHEW LTD
Rattlesden
Bury St Edmunds
Suffolk IP30 0SZ

Phone 0449 737978
Fax 0449 737834

Please ask for our complete catalogue of outstanding Church Music.

Front Cover: *St. Clare as Patron Saint of Embroidery*
by Edward Reginald Frampton (1872-1923).
Private collection. Reproduced by kind permission.

Cover designed by Graham Johnstone.
Picture Research: Jane Rayson.

First published in Great Britain in 1992 by Kevin Mayhew Ltd

© Copyright 1992 Kevin Mayhew Ltd

ISBN 0 86209 295 7

Printed and bound in Great Britain.

Contents

About the Composer

COLIN MAWBY is a pre-eminent composer of liturgical music for the English speaking churches. In addition to an ever-increasing list of published works, he regularly receives commissions from major Cathedrals, Festivals and broadcasting authorities. He has also written secular music, including five song cycles. Performances of his music are given all over the world.

He is Choral Director for Radio Telefís Éireann, the national broadcasting authority in the Republic of Ireland, where he is responsible for training the radio station's four choirs. Previously, he was Master of Music at Westminster Cathedral. His experience of choirs and his sympathy with singers is apparent in his tuneful and immensely singable writing.

As a performing musician, Colin Mawby has appeared at many music festivals and the BBC Promenade Concerts. He also makes regular broadcasts on radio and television and records with the major labels. He has conducted groups such as the London Mozart Players, the Wren Orchestra, Pro Cantione Antiqua, the Belgian Radio Choir and the BBC Singers.

Also by Colin Mawby:

Organ Music   *Quiet-Time Music*
                   Fanfares & Finales

Choral Music   *Invocation*
                   Communion Songs
                   Songs for Many Seasons
                   In Memory Of Me
                   Festival Mass

Other music by Colin Mawby is available in numerous collections published by Kevin Mayhew Ltd.

A REFLECTIVE IMPROVISATION

Colin Mawby

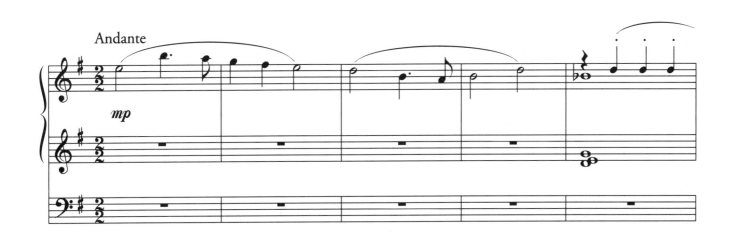

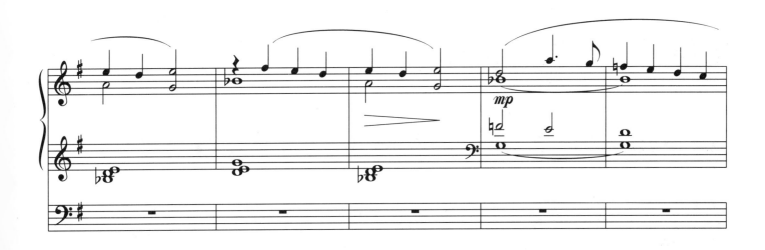

A JOYFUL IMPROVISATION

Colin Mawby

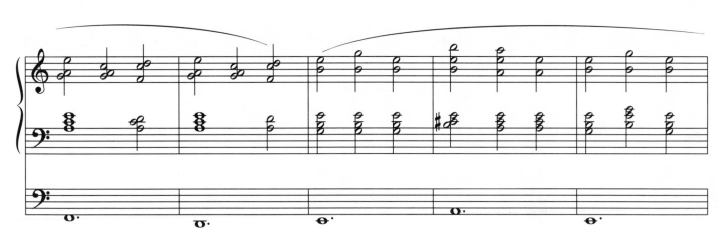

A FESTAL IMPROVISATION

Colin Mawby

Allegro

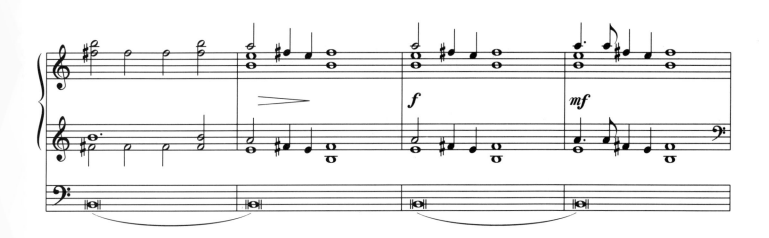

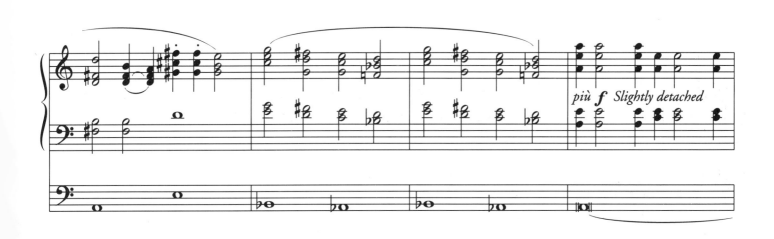

A CALM IMPROVISATION

Colin Mawby

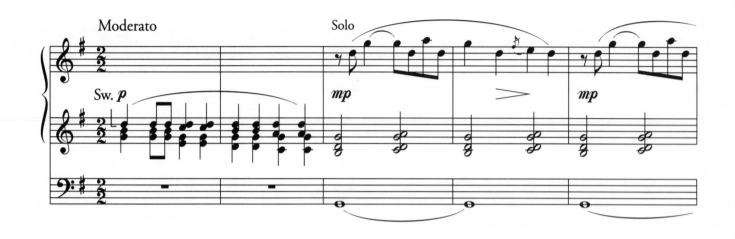

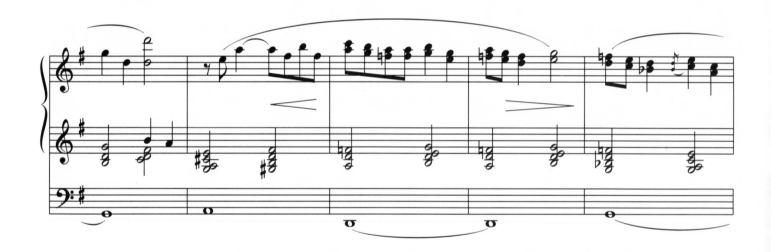

A HAPPY IMPROVISATION

Colin Mawby

17

AN INTROSPECTIVE IMPROVISATION

Colin Mawby

A JUBILANT IMPROVISATION

Colin Mawby

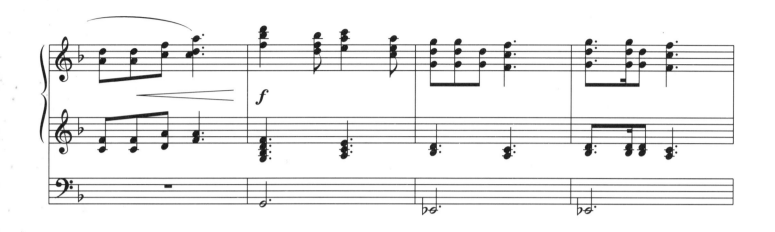

A PEACEFUL IMPROVISATION

Colin Mawby

A RUGGED IMPROVISATION

Colin Mawby

Con Moto

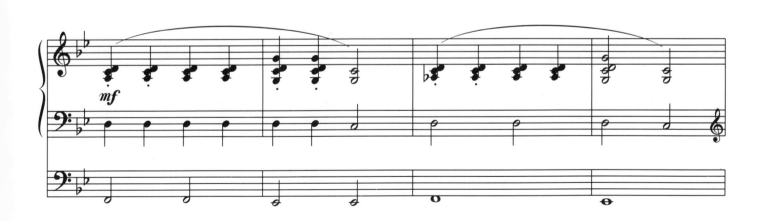

A FORCEFUL IMPROVISATION

Colin Mawby

Maestoso

Tuba

A MEDITATIVE IMPROVISATION

Colin Mawby

Andante
Solo

A POWERFUL IMPROVISATION

Colin Mawby

A LIVELY IMPROVISATION

Colin Mawby

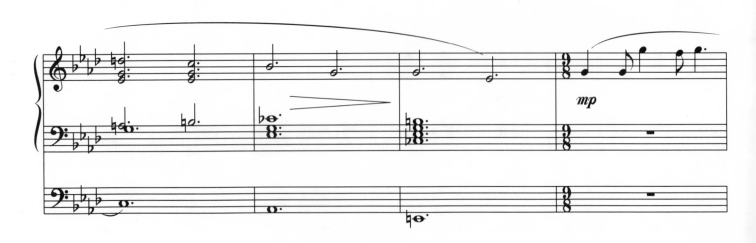

rit.   a tempo
Solo

42

43

AN EXULTANT IMPROVISATION

Colin Mawby

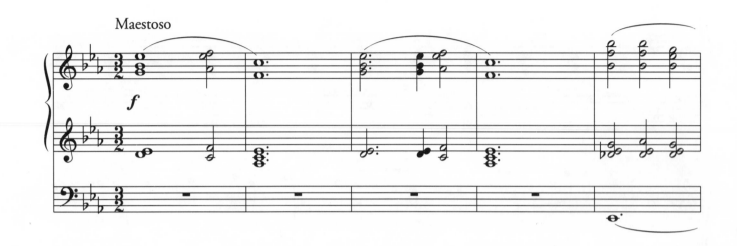

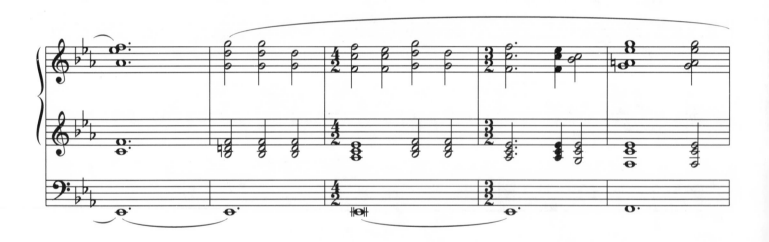

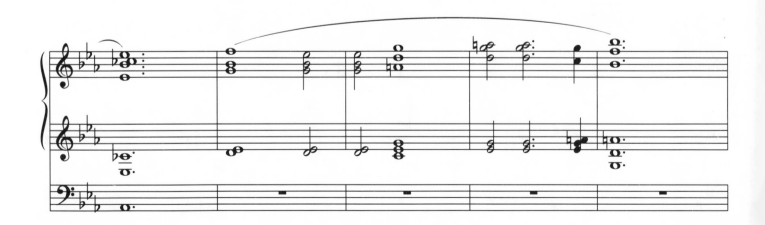

44

ANOTHER REFLECTIVE IMPROVISATION

Colin Mawby

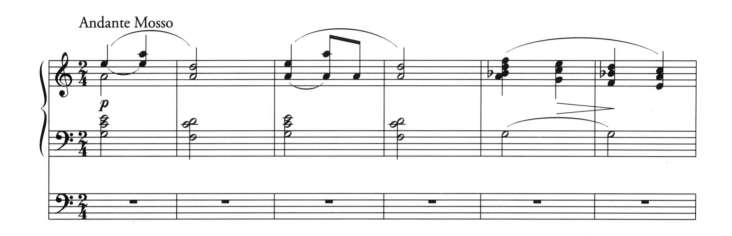

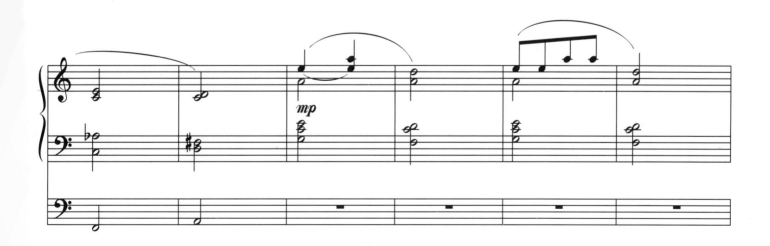